TO WEE OR NOT TO WEE!

PAMELA BUTCHART

nosy crow

Look out for:

BABY ALIENS GOT MY TEACHER!

THE SPY WHO LOVED SCHOOL DINNERS

MY HEADTEACHER IS A VAMPIRE RAT!

ATTACK OF THE DEMON DINNER LADIES

For Marina

First published in the UK in 2016 by Nosy Crow Ltd
The Crow's Nest, 14 Baden Place, Crosby Row
London, SE1 1YW, UK

Macbeth first featured on BBC Learning School Radio as *Macdeath*

5 7 9 10 8 6

A CIP catalogue record for this book will be available from the British Library.

Printed and bound in the UK by Clays Ltd, St. Ives Plc

Papers used by Nosy Crow are made from wood grown in
sustainable forests.

ISBN: 978 0 85763 772 7

www.nosycrow.com

Contents

HAMLET

HAMLET, Prince of Denmark
GERTRUDE, Hamlet's mum, Queen of Denmark
CLAUDIUS, Hamlet's uncle, the dead King's brother
HORATIO, Hamlet's best friend
THE GHOST, Hamlet's dad, once King of Denmark
OPHELIA, Hamlet's girlfriend
THE ACTORS, who perform Hamlet's play
POLONIUS, Ophelia's dad and Claudius's best friend
THE GRAVEDIGGERS
YORICK, once the court jester, now a skull
LAERTES, Polonius's son, and Ophelia's brother
FORTINBRAS, Prince of Norway

One time when we were playing Monopoly at Maisie's house we couldn't even get started because Zach COULD NOT decide if he wanted to be the hat or the car. And he kept saying stuff like, "But I like both. What should I do?" and "What if I pick the car and then I lose?" and "What if Jodi gets the car and she wins?"

Then Maisie's mum came in and asked us if we would like pepperoni on our pizza and I said yes and so did Maisie and Jodi but Zach said that he wasn't sure. And then he put his head in his hands because he couldn't decide about the car OR the hat OR

the pepperoni and it was

STRESSING HIM OUT.

So that's when I told Zach that he was being EXACTLY like HAMLET out of the Shakespeare play. And Zach said that he WASN'T and Maisie's mum burst out laughing and said that he was, actually. Then Zach said that he

So I asked Zach if he knew who Hamlet was

and he said he didn't.

So that's when I told Zach that Hamlet was the Prince of Denmark who had been at university for about twenty years because he couldn't decide what to be when he grew up so just kept going back to college and doing **LOADS** of stuff like history and biology and hairdressing.

But one day when Hamlet came home to get his mum to do his washing for him he found out that his dad, the King of Denmark, had died. And then his mum told him that she was going on a date with his Uncle Claudius and that there was some left-over lasagne in the fridge.

Hamlet was FURIOUS because his mum didn't even seem BOTHERED that his dad had died and also because she was going on a date with HIS UNCLE (which was TOTALLY WEIRD even though she was pretending that it wasn't).

Hamlet's mum and his Uncle Claudius got back from their date JUST in time for the king's funeral and as SOON as the funeral finished Claudius went down on one knee and PROPOSED to Hamlet's mum! Then he told all the funeral guests to just stay sitting down because they were about to

get MARRIED and he was going to be the KING OF DENMARK!

Hamlet was totally SHOCKED because his uncle was about to become his STEPDAD

and also because HE was supposed to become King of Denmark. And he probably should have grabbed the minister's microphone and shouted, "Mum! You CAN'T marry Dad's BROTHER! That's disgusting!" and also "I'M THE KING NOW!"

But Hamlet didn't shout any of those things. He just sat there trying to decide what to do to stop the wedding until the minister said, "I now pronounce you husband and wife," and it was too late.

After the Funeral-Wedding Hamlet went up to the castle roof and moaned for HOURS to his best friend, Horatio (who was

very good at listening, which was a good thing because Hamlet talked a LOT).

Hamlet kept asking Horatio LOADS of questions like "What do you think I should do about the King thing?" and "Should I get the castle locks changed so Claudius can't move in?" and "Should I become a hairdresser?"

But Horatio never got a chance to answer ANY of the questions because as SOON as Hamlet asked a question he ALWAYS asked ANOTHER one right away (which was very annoying).

But then all of a sudden a ghostly voice

said, "You've been eating MY lasagne! I can smell it on your breath."

And Hamlet

GASPED

because he KNEW it was his Ghost Dad before he even turned around because lasagne was his dad's most favourite thing.

Once the ghost stopped going on about never being able to eat lasagne EVER again, he said, "Hamlet, I am here to tell you that I was MURDERED by my own BROTHER!"

And then the ghost told Hamlet that Claudius had crept up on him when he was sleeping in the garden and poured POISON in his EAR! And that his ear was still a bit sore and itchy even though he was dead.

And then he said, "I need you to do two VERY IMPORTANT things for me. And you must do them because I am your Ghost Dad."

That's when he told Hamlet that he must AVENGE his death (which meant he wanted him to kill his uncle) and also that he was to bring him some lasagne so he could smell it and try to lick the air. And then he disappeared.

"What are you going to do?" said Horatio.

But Hamlet said that he didn't know and

that he needed a drink of juice first.

Then when he'd had his juice Horatio said, "What are you going to DO, Hamlet?" But Hamlet said that he wasn't sure and that he needed to finish his jigsaw first (even though he probably shouldn't have started a jigsaw when he was in the middle of trying to decide if he was going avenge his Ghost Dad's death).

So Horatio waited until Hamlet finished his jigsaw and then asked him AGAIN. But Hamlet spotted a pigeon and said he needed to draw a picture of it first before he decided what to do. So Horatio just stopped asking

him because he was **OBVIOUSLY** avoiding the question and had **NO IDEA** what he was going to do because he was a bit of a nightmare like that.

Hamlet could **NEVER** make his mind up about **ANYTHING**. And one time he actually went to school in just his pants and got sent home because he couldn't decide what to wear.

Hamlet said he needed to be sure the ghost was telling the truth before he did the avenging and that he was going to

on his uncle to see if he was acting all GUILTY and SUSPICIOUS like a Brother Murderer would.

So Hamlet decided to PRETEND he was in a terrible mood and be MEAN to EVERYONE, even his girlfriend Ophelia, so that they would be so shocked by his bad behaviour that they wouldn't notice the

Hamlet coughed on ALL the scrambled eggs at breakfast, left ALL the royal toilet seats up and made up a song about Claudius's best friend Polonius looking like an evil guinea pig and sang it to him (even though Polonius was Ophelia's dad so that was a bit of a bad idea).

EVERYONE was talking about how RUDE

Hamlet was now. And when anyone caught him SPYING on his uncle he would just call them the WORST name he could think of and they'd forget all about the spying.

And when poor Ophelia asked Hamlet if he still wanted to marry her, Hamlet said that he DEFINITELY DIDN'T and that she should probably just go away and become a NUN and that made Ophelia run away crying because she

Hamlet and also because she'd already

bought her wedding dress and it was non-refundable.

That's when Hamlet realised that he didn't have to pretend to be in a terrible mood any more because he really WAS in a terrible mood because he kept thinking about MURDER and AVENGING all the time and he couldn't make up his mind about Claudius.

But one day, Hamlet got an IDEA while he was watching the Royal Actors rehearse. Watching the actors rehearse was one of his and Horatio's favourite things to do because the actors were TERRIBLE and always forgot their lines so it was a good laugh. And sometimes their wigs slipped down their faces while they were talking and they just had to leave them there because it was a DRESS REHEARSAL, which means you can't stop even if your wig is covering

your face and no one can hear what you're saying.

So anyway, Hamlet's IDEA was to write a NEW PLAY about a man who kills a king by pouring poison in his ear while he's sleeping and to make the actors do that one to see if Claudius would

when he saw it.

But the actors didn't want to do it because there were loads of spelling mistakes in the script because Hamlet had had to write it

really quickly. So Hamlet showed the actors a bag of gold and a voucher he got for his birthday for an all-you-can-eat Chinese buffet and the actors said they'd do it.

Hamlet STARED at Claudius while he watched the play (which was pretty hard to do because Claudius kept making kissy sounds at Hamlet's mum and pinching her cheeks, which made Hamlet feel violently sick).

But then Claudius STOPPED making kissy sounds and leaned forwards in his seat as he watched one of the actors pour poison into the sleeping king's ear.

Claudius went as white as a SHEET and shouted,

and then he ran away.

THAT'S when Hamlet knew that the ghost WAS his Ghost Dad and that it had been telling the TRUTH about the Brother Murderer.

Everything got a bit out of hand after that. Hamlet's mum started screaming and crying (even though she had no idea what was going on and she was just being SUPER dramatic) so Hamlet told her to go to her room and that he'd meet her there in a minute because he had to go to the toilet first.

But Hamlet DIDN'T go to the toilet because he didn't need to go and he'd only pretended that he needed to go because he was on his way to KILL CLAUDIUS and AVENGE his father's death!

Hamlet found Claudius praying with his eyes closed so he raised his dagger in the air. But then he changed his mind. He didn't really want to kill anyone while they were saying their prayers, but he DID want to avenge his dad. And then he thought maybe he actually DID need a wee! So he ran to the bathroom but then stopped halfway and cried, "To WEE or NOT to wee? That is the question!" because he wasn't sure.

Hamlet talked to himself for half an hour until he'd forgotten what he was doing there. And then he went to see his mum for a cuddle because his brain was hurting.

But Gertrude wouldn't give him a cuddle because he tried to tell her what Claudius was REALLY like and she didn't like hearing that so she kept covering her ears and saying,

"LA LA LA LA
I'M NOT
LISTENING
TO YOU
LA LA LA LA LA!"

And when Hamlet tried to take her hands off her ears she SCREAMED THE WHOLE

PALACE DOWN because she was probably the most dramatic person that had ever lived.

Then Hamlet noticed something moving behind one of the curtains and he thought it was Claudius SPYING on them so he took his dagger and stuck it RIGHT THROUGH the curtain. But it wasn't Claudius. It was Polonius, Claudius's best friend and

Ophelia's dad, who had been spying. And now he was dead. But to be fair, that **HAD** been a pretty stupid place to stand. So it wasn't really **ALL** Hamlet's fault.

That's when Hamlet's mum looked a bit sad for Hamlet and it was probably because Hamlet just couldn't do anything right. I mean, **FINALLY** he made a decision and curtain-stabbed someone and it wasn't even the **RIGHT** person!

Hamlet tried to get out of it by saying that he thought he'd heard a rat, and that he'd been trying to stab that. But nobody believed him. So he left the castle for a bit.

But then Hamlet found out that Ophelia had been so upset about her dad that she'd run away and tripped and fallen into a river and died. And he got so upset that he just began wandering around graveyards with Horatio because he was getting a bit OBSESSED with killing and dead people and worms. And it didn't help when he saw a SKULL.

"Whose wormy skull is that?" he asked

the gravediggers.

"That's Yorick, your dad's old jester from years ago when you were a baby."

Well, as SOON as the gravediggers said that Hamlet screamed, "I KNEW HIM, HORATIO!" and jumped RIGHT into the grave and began SPEAKING to the skull and asking it loads of questions like, "What should I do about EVERYTHING?" and just, "Why?" And then he told it he really finally did need a wee.

But by now Hamlet was SO BAD at making ANY decisions that he couldn't even decide whether he should get out of the wormy

grave and go to the toilet or not. So he just stood there in the grave wailing at the skull and asking for its opinion.

But then the gravediggers said that they'd had enough and that he had better NOT wee in the grave because they weren't actually finished digging it yet. So Hamlet said sorry and got out.

That's when he saw his mum and Claudius. And Polonius's son, Laertes, was there too. And when he saw Hamlet he said that he was going to BATTER him because of his dad and sister.

Before Hamlet even had a chance to

BLINK Laertes jumped on him because Laertes was not like Hamlet. Laertes just did things and didn't really think about them first. But Laertes probably SHOULD have thought about it a bit because he jumped on Hamlet so hard that they both ended up in the grave, covered in worms, and Hamlet even weed himself a bit.

Laertes jumped out of the grave because he didn't want to get wee on his new trousers and then he challenged Hamlet to a SWORD FIGHT back at the castle, once Hamlet had got changed.

Claudius LOVED the idea of the sword

fight because he wanted Hamlet dead. So he told Laertes to cover his sword with POISON because he was obsessed with killing people with poison. And he even had a poisoned glass of wine ready to give to Hamlet in case the sword didn't work.

As soon as Hamlet had changed his trousers Claudius gave him a rubbish sword and told him good luck.

There was a

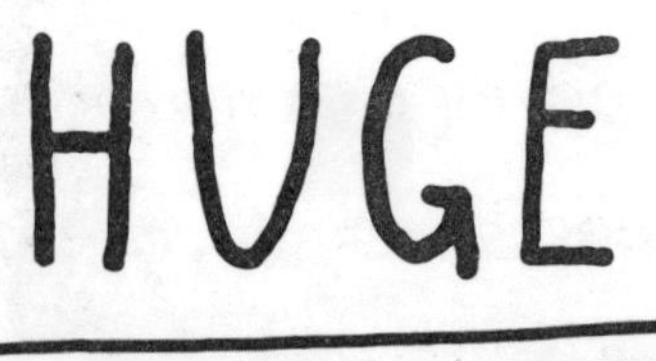

crowd waiting and some of them were

pointing at Hamlet because he was wearing pyjama bottoms since that's all he'd been able to find at the castle because someone (probably Claudius) had chucked out all his trousers.

Hamlet looked up at his mum and she waved LOADS and shouted down that she loved him and that she hoped he won. But then Claudius kissed her on the lips for ages so she would stop saying nice things to Hamlet because he didn't like it.

Hamlet tried to tell Laertes that he hadn't actually meant to stab his dad through a curtain, and that it had been a bit of an accident, but Laertes was too ANGRY to listen. He swung his sword and cut Hamlet's finger. So Hamlet fought back as hard as he could with the rubbish sword. And he did so well that Laertes tripped and sliced his leg with his OWN sword.

Gertrude got a bit excited that her son was doing so well so she picked up the glass Claudius had meant for Hamlet and said,

"Cheers to my son!"

"NOOOOOOOOOOOOO!"

shouted Claudius. But it was too late. Hamlet's mum gulped down the WHOLE glass because fizzy wine was her favourite and she hadn't had any since Christmas.

Just then Hamlet realised that the cut on his finger was burning and that the burning was spreading up his arm and into his chest. He looked at the cut on Laertes' leg and saw that he was in serious pain too.

Then Laertes fell dramatically to

the ground and cried, "The King is a

Then Hamlet's mum clutched her throat and toppled off her throne into the buffet.

And that's when Hamlet realised that they were ALL poisoned and that it was ALL CLAUDIUS'S FAULT!

So that's when Hamlet EVENTUALLY

decided to avenge his Ghost Dad's murder and he poison-stabbed Claudius!

And then Hamlet died too.

But then he opened his eyes and said, "Horatio. Will you tell the story of me and what happened to me for ever, even if it makes you cry?"

And Horatio said that he would.

And then Hamlet died again.

But then he opened his eyes AGAIN and said, "Horatio. Do you think I would have been a good hairdresser?"

And Horatio said that he thought he would have been, even though he didn't really mean it because his hair was still longer on one side than it was on the other from when he'd let Hamlet cut it. But that wasn't the right time to bring it up.

And then Hamlet died again.

But he kept opening his eyes and saying more things because even when he was

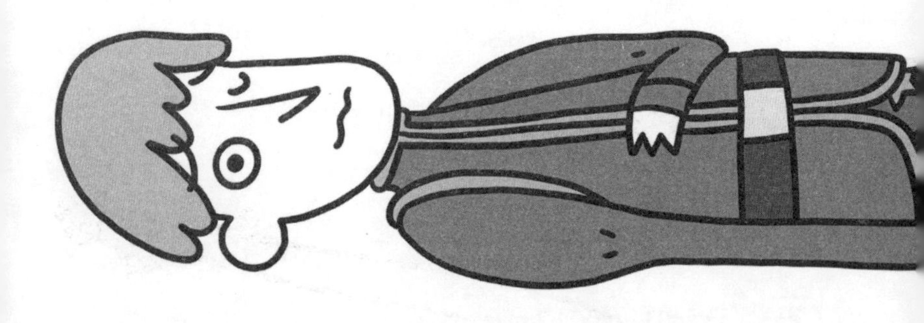

almost dead Hamlet could **NOT** stop talking and saying one more thing and it went on like that for about forty-five minutes.

Once Hamlet was **DEFINITELY DEAD** the Prince of Norway, who was called Fortinbras, came to be the king. And he let Horatio and loads of homeless people live in

the palace too because he was a really nice person.

And even though Horatio never saw the ghost of Hamlet or Hamlet's dad again, he always made lasagne on a Thursday and left two bowls in the spooky bit of the castle before he went to bed.

When I finished the story, Jodi looked at Zach and said, "Zach. Do you want to end up like Hamlet?"

And Zach's eyes went REALLY WIDE. And then

he said that he was DEFINITELY going to be the HAT and that he DEFINITELY wanted pepperoni on his pizza. And also that he was going to decide EVERYTHING from now on.

So I said, "Great! What film do you want to watch later then?"

And Zach didn't say anything and then he said he needed to go to the toilet. And we all KNEW it was because he couldn't decide.

And we all burst out laughing and couldn't stop. Especially when Maisie squealed, "TO WEE OR NOT TO WEE, ZACH? THAT IS THE QUESTION!"

MACBETH

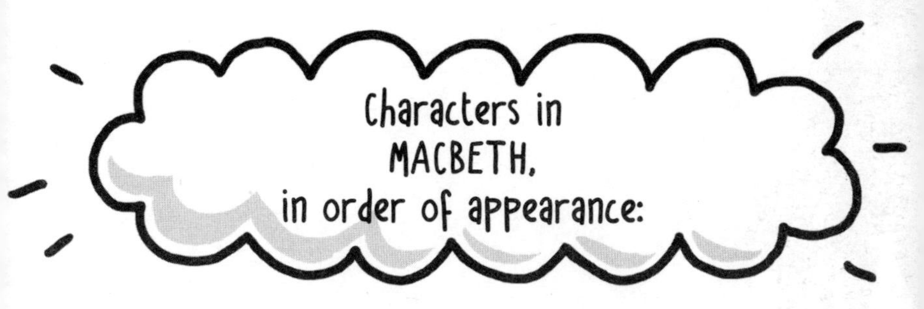

MACBETH, soldier and wannabe King of Scotland
BANQUO, Macbeth's best friend
THE THREE WITCHES, one tall, one beardy, one with a weird eye
KING DUNCAN, the King of Scotland
MALCOLM, King Duncan's son
LADY MACBETH (aka "Bethy"), wife of Macbeth and buffet provider
MACDUFF, King Duncan's best friend and sworn enemy of Macbeth

One time our teacher, Miss Jones, said she would tell us ANY STORY WE WANTED for our Friday treat.

So I put my hand up and asked for the story of *Macbeth* by William Shakespeare. But then Gary Petrie said that Shakespeare was BORING and that he wanted a story that was NOT boring and was also SCARY.

So that's when I said that *Macbeth* WASN'T boring, actually. And that it was probably the SCARIEST story EVER because it had WITCHES and BLOOD and people getting their HEADS CHOPPED OFF.

And that's when Gary Petrie and everyone else BEGGED Miss Jones to tell us the story of *Macbeth*.

But Miss Jones said, "Um, how about something else? Something with less blood, perhaps?"

But we said no.

So Miss Jones said that she didn't know the story of *Macbeth* well enough to tell it. But we all KNEW that she was

LYING

because she wanted us to have a story with LESS BLOOD.

So I put my hand up and told Miss Jones that I could tell everyone the story because I knew it ALL.

Miss Jones looked a bit annoyed, but she said yes anyway, because she didn't really have a choice because everyone was looking at me and I'd already told Jodi to shut the curtains and put the lights off.

So that's when I told everyone that Macbeth was a STRONG soldier who ate six bowls of porridge and twenty pieces of toast every morning for his breakfast and that he could chop FOUR HEADS OFF with just ONE swing of his sword.

And that one day, Macbeth heard that an army from Norway was coming to Scotland to fight them.

So Macbeth had a DOUBLE breakfast that morning and then went and got his best friend, Banquo, and they snuck up on the Norwegians and chopped ALL their heads off in less than twenty minutes. And even though there were HUNDREDS of Norwegians Macbeth and Banquo still won because they were very good at BATTLES because they'd been playing SWORDS since they were at primary school.

But then on their way home three weird

witches appeared out of the mist.

One was as tall as a tree, one had a weird eye that looked a bit like a tadpole and the other one had a beard.

"ALL HAIL MACBETH. FOR HE WILL BE KING!" they chanted.

Macbeth was SHOCKED when he heard that because he knew that witches can see the FUTURE.

But he was also excited because he had ALWAYS wanted to be king.

But then the witches turned to Banquo and said, "Your son will be king after Macbeth."

Macbeth didn't like that as much, because

he didn't like hearing about people that weren't him becoming king.

When King Duncan heard that Macbeth had won the battle he was SO PLEASED that he said he was going to come and stay over at Macbeth's house and bring his friends, including Macduff, who was his very best friend, and his son, Malcolm, and have a party (which was a bit cheeky because no one had invited him, but he was the KING so he could do what he liked).

Lady Macbeth was raging because she had to go shopping and get decorations and do a buffet and she only had an hour to do it

because they didn't have phones in Olden Times so she only found out about the king coming when Macbeth came home, covered in guts, and told her.

That night, the king made a big announcement. He said that he was SO PROUD of someone that they were to be the next king.

EVERYONE thought Duncan was going to say Macbeth's name and they kept looking at Macbeth and winking at him. But that's NOT what the king said. He said that his son, MALCOLM, would be the next king.

That REALLY annoyed Macbeth because

HE wanted to be king. Plus, Duncan had said it in front of

EVERYONE

so it was a bit embarrassing (especially because Macbeth cried a bit).

Lady Macbeth took him into a different room and gave him a tissue made of cloth and told him to stop being such a big baby because she had a plan to take care of it but that she wouldn't tell him if he didn't stop crying, so he stopped.

That's when Lady Macbeth said that she

thought Macbeth should MURDER King Duncan that night when he was sleeping on their sofa bed and then blame it on Duncan's son, Malcolm.

But Macbeth said, "You've gone MAD, Bethy!" (That's what Macbeth called his wife because it takes quite a long time to say "Lady Macbeth" all the time, and also because he thought it was cute.)

But Lady Macbeth said she HADN'T gone mad and that if Macbeth killed Duncan and blamed it on Malcolm then Malcolm would probably run away and hide and Macbeth would be KING.

Macbeth got butterflies in his tummy when Lady Macbeth said that he would be king because it was something he

about. Sometimes when Lady Macbeth went to the shops he'd make himself a crown out of kitchen roll and prance about the house saying stuff like, "I am THE KING. Make me a toastie or I'll chop your head off!"

So anyway, Macbeth said that he wasn't sure about murdering King Duncan because he'd be in BIG TROUBLE if he got caught.

But then Lady Macbeth started saying loads of stuff like, "A REAL king is BRAVE," and "You're not a big scaredy-cat, ARE you?"

Lady Macbeth had ALWAYS been sneaky like that. She'd always managed to convince people to do stuff for her and give her their crisps.

So Macbeth said, "Fine. I'll do it," because he didn't want Lady Macbeth to call him names any more.

So that night Lady Macbeth gave King Duncan's guards some wine that had a SLEEPING POTION in it and the guards fell into a DEEP SLEEP.

She took their daggers and left them in the king's bedchamber for Macbeth to find later.

Then Lady Macbeth sent Macbeth to kill

the king while he slept, but that's when Macbeth started PANICKING and saying that he couldn't do it. So Lady Macbeth did her

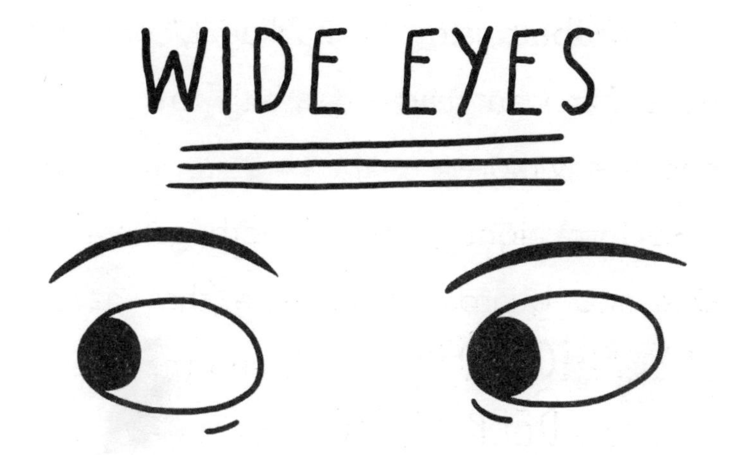

at him and that really scared him, so he went. But when Macbeth was creeping down the corridor he saw a FLOATING GHOST

DAGGER and when he reached out for it, his hand went right through it and Macbeth got such a fright he started crying because he didn't like ghost stuff.

When Macbeth eventually opened his eyes again he saw that the ghost dagger was pointing towards the king's room. So he knew it was a

So Macbeth did the murder and then

he ran back to Lady Macbeth, covered in blood. Lady Macbeth almost had KITTENS when she saw that Macbeth had brought the MURDER WEAPONS back with him because she had SPECIFICALLY TOLD HIM to leave the daggers in the guards' hands so it looked like

done it.

But that's when Macbeth completely LOST IT and started crying and shaking and saying that he didn't want to be a murderer any more, even though it was a bit late for that. So Lady Macbeth locked him in the bathroom and put the daggers in the sleeping guards' hands herself. And she even smeared some of the knife-blood on their faces so it looked like they'd done the murder because she was very crafty and evil.

The next morning the king's best friend, Macduff, screamed,

My king has been murdered!"

Lady Macbeth RAN out of her bedroom in her jammies and said, "MALCOLM told the guards to kill his father. I know it!"

And then she nudged Macbeth really hard in the ribs, and Macbeth nodded.

So Malcolm RAN out of Macbeth's house as FAST as he could because he knew no one was going to believe him because it was two against one.

Then everyone shouted,

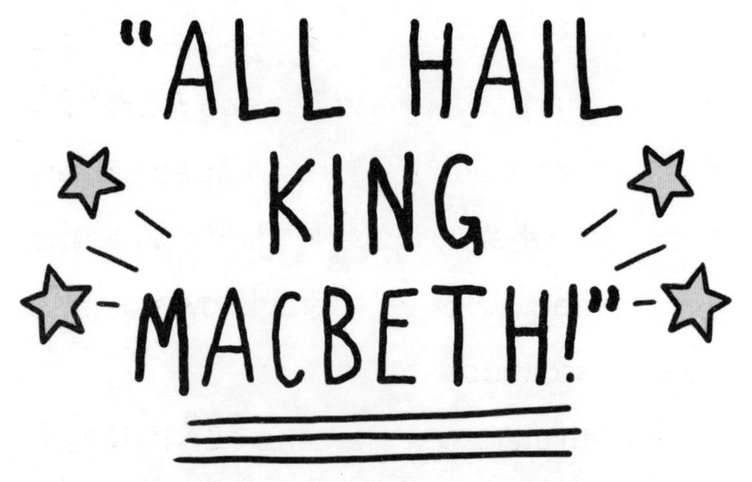

just as Lady Macbeth said they would.

But as soon as Macbeth got to the palace

and put the crown on he started having DARK THOUGHTS about what the witches had said about Banquo's son becoming king. So Macbeth sent murderers to kill Banquo and his son, Fleance, which is TERRIBLE because Banquo had been his best friend since primary school and Banquo ALWAYS stuck up for Macbeth and swapped sweets with him when Macbeth didn't like the ones he had. What he didn't know was that Fleance escaped...

Macbeth started to become SERIOUSLY WEIRD after that. He began having HALLUCINATIONS because he felt MEGA

GUILTY about being a king-murderer AND a best friend-murderer. And that night when Lady Macbeth was slumbering he just lay there WIDE AWAKE. And it wasn't because of Lady Macbeth snoring like a gorilla, it was because Macbeth's brain was

by all the terrible things he had done to become king.

But Lady Macbeth wasn't really bothered about what she'd done. As soon as she'd got to the palace she'd tried on ALL the royal dresses and made the servants peel her ONE HUNDRED grapes, even though she didn't like grapes, and then she threw every single one in the bin while they watched, because that's just what she was like.

Macbeth had a big party to celebrate becoming king. There was food and wine and everyone was up dancing and having a great laugh. But not Macbeth. He just sat there looking miserable while Lady Macbeth sang on the karaoke.

Then when Macbeth was cutting his King Cake, he thought he saw BANQUO and he shouted, "GET HIM OFF MY THRONE!"

But no one else could see Banquo so it was all a bit embarrassing.

Macbeth started running around, wailing and saying **LOADS** of weird stuff and crying a bit too, and that's when Lady Macbeth had to send everyone home early without any cake.

Once everyone had gone Lady Macbeth said, "What's **WRONG** with you? Is your crown too tight or something?!"

But Macbeth wasn't listening because he was too busy shouting at a piece of cake he thought was Banquo.

Later that night, Macbeth went wandering

in the hills in his nightie and woke up the three weird witches with all his wailing.

The witches could see that Macbeth was in a bit of a state, and they were keen to get back to their witchy beds, so they got the cauldron out.

"Look deep into the potion!" said the one with the beard.

So Macbeth looked into the cauldron and that's when the face of King Duncan came floating out and said,

Then Banquo's head floated RIGHT UP to Macbeth's face and hissed, "No one born of a woman can kill you."

Both of the heads got bigger and bigger and BIGGER until they popped and

SPLATTERED Macbeth.

But Macbeth just LAUGHED because he was in a good mood now since he knew that EVERYONE is born of women, because men can't have babies, so that meant that NO ONE could kill him.

But then he heard a whisper coming from the witch with the tadpole eye.

Macbeth

at the witch's lips because although they were shut tight, somehow she was still able to speak.

"SHUSH!" said Macbeth to the other witches who were cackling about his nightie. And that's when Macbeth heard the witch say: "You will be king until Birnam Wood walks to your castle."

Macbeth laughed and said, "Then I'll be king FOR EVER because trees can't walk!"

Macbeth RAN back to the castle to lock Macduff in the dungeon because of what King Duncan's floating cauldron-head had said. But his servants told him that Macduff had already FLED and was probably MILES away by now because he'd taken a HUGE packed lunch.

And THAT'S when Macbeth

COMPLETELY FREAKED OUT.

He should have just sat down for a minute and done a sudoku or something to calm down. But he didn't. He ordered Macduff's house to be burned to the ground and his whole family murdered. Which was obviously a MEGA overreaction, but that was just what Macbeth was like now. He had completely changed since he heard he couldn't be killed. He wasn't scared OR nervous any more. He'd become a TYRANT.

Lady Macbeth was

when she found out what Macbeth had been getting up to without telling her because usually SHE was the one in charge.

Then Lady Macbeth started to feel GUILTY about the murders and she kept seeing the ghosts of Macduff's children when she was trying to eat her cereal, and trying to wash blood off her hands every five minutes, even though there wasn't any there.

Lady Macbeth got really sick after that and eventually died of guilt.

When Macbeth heard about his Bethy he was sad, but he didn't cry because he wasn't the type of king who cried any more.

Then one of the guards came rushing up to the castle and shouted, "Macduff is on his way to kill you! He's brought the ENGLISH ARMY!"

But Macbeth just LAUGHED and shouted back, "I'll believe it when I see Birnam Wood WALK!"

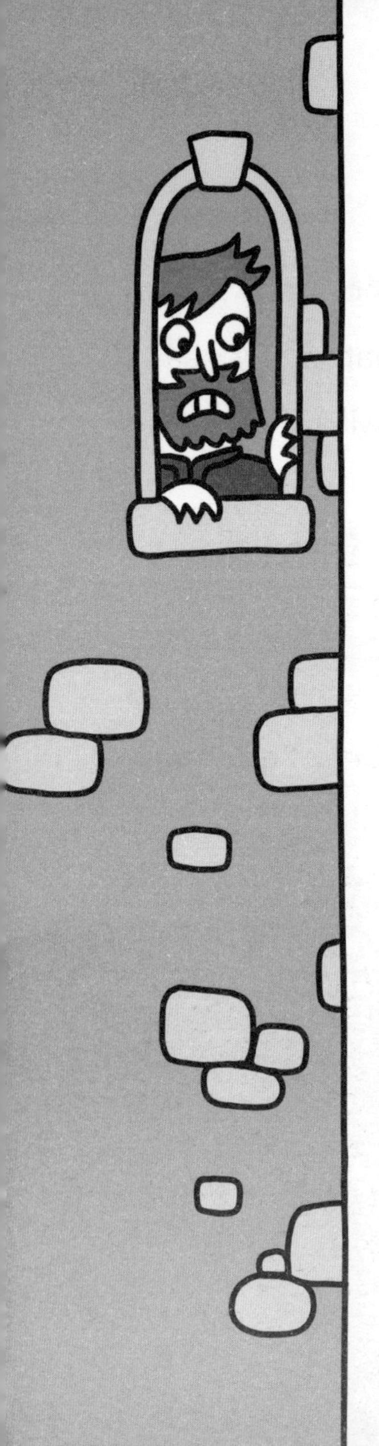

But when Macbeth looked out of the window the next morning he saw that the trees WERE moving. And that's when he realised that the army were using BRANCHES to hide behind.

So Macbeth put his slippers on and RAN towards the army because he knew that he couldn't be killed.

Then Macbeth started chopping EVERYONE'S

heads off until there were no more heads. But then MACDUFF appeared and said, "You killed my family. Now I will kill YOU and Malcolm will be king."

"HA!" said Macbeth. "NO ONE born of a woman can kill ME!"

And that's when Macduff pulled out his sword and said, "I am not born of a woman, Macbeth. My mum died before I was born. The doctors cut me from her tummy to save me."

And then Macduff raised his sword and sliced Macbeth's head clean off and watched it roll down the hill into the duck pond. And Malcolm did become king, and so did Banquo's son, Fleance, years later. So it just goes to show that the weird witches knew what they were talking about.

I looked round at all my friends. "But that's not the end of the story," I said. "Macduff went and got Macbeth's head and put it on top of a SPEAR outside Glamis Castle, where it can still be seen today!"

That's when Miss Jones told me off for making that last bit up because Gary Petrie's gran was taking him to Glamis Castle that weekend and he looked TERRIFIED.

So I asked if I could say ONE last thing. And before Miss Jones could say no I used my hair for a beard and started chanting:

"Double, double toil and trouble; Fire burn, and cauldron bubble..."

And Gary Petrie started screaming!

A MIDSUMMER
NIGHT'S
DREAM

Characters in A MIDSUMMER NIGHT'S DREAM, in order of appearance:

HERMIA, betrothed to Demetrius,
in love with Lysander
DEMETRIUS, betrothed to Hermia,
in love with himself
LYSANDER, in love with Hermia,
who loves him back
HELENA, in love with Demetrius
OBERON, King of the Fairies, married to Titania
TITANIA, Queen of the Fairies, married to Oberon
PUCK, a naughty elf who serves Oberon
NICK BOTTOM, an actor Titania falls in love with

When Gary Petrie asked Jodi to dance with him at the School Charity Dance and Jodi said **YES** we were all **SHOCKED** because Gary Petrie usually has **BOGEY FINGERS** from picking his nose and also because we didn't realise that Jodi **LIKED** him.

Maisie had to sit down on the ground because it was so horrible and also because there weren't any chairs because the teachers wanted us to dance and not just sit down and watch. We all STARED at Jodi with our mouths wide open as she whizzed around the dinner hall with Gary Petrie.

And then Zach said, "Do you think Gary Petrie is her boyfriend now?" And Maisie said that she thought he WAS because Jodi looked like she was enjoying the dancing and she was smiling loads.

But I just KNEW that there was something WEIRD going on because Jodi did not usually like Gary Petrie and she was smiling TOO MUCH.

So I said, "Something isn't right. I think Jodi might have been

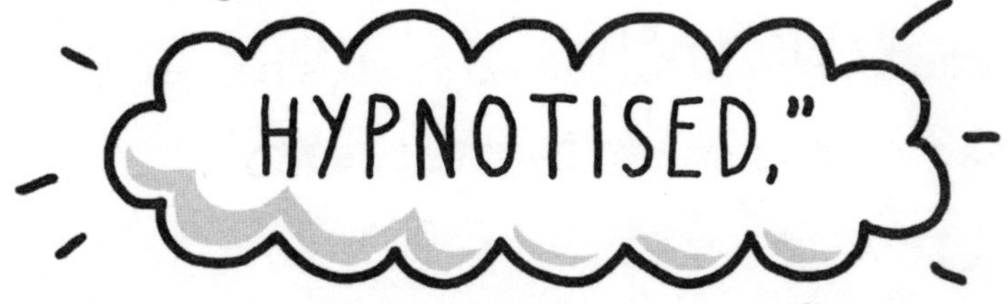
HYPNOTISED,"

because I couldn't think of any reason other than HYPNOTISM or ACTUAL MAGIC for why Jodi was dancing with Gary Petrie when she hadn't even been made to do it by a teacher.

And that's when Maisie

and said, "You're RIGHT. It IS magic. Jodi's been BEWITCHED! Like in that Shakespeare play, *A Midsummer Night's Dream*!"

And then I GASPED because I knew Maisie was RIGHT because this was EXACTLY like what happens in the play.

Because *A Midsummer Night's Dream* is all about

and a WEIRD FAIRY ROYAL FAMILY and a CREEPY ELF and someone called BOTTOM. And it's probably one of the WEIRDEST plays Shakespeare or anyone ever did.

But Zach said he didn't know the story and that I needed to tell him about it NOW so that we could find out what to do and save Jodi.

So that's when I told Zach that the play took place in ANCIENT GREECE and that there was a weird FAIRY WORLD just across the road from the city of Athens and that you had to be quite careful if your horse and chariot broke down there because the fairies were a bit CREEPY and liked to meddle in everyone's lives rather than just minding their own business.

I explained that in the REAL WORLD of Athens there was a bit of a

going on, like the kind of stuff that goes on in the TV programmes that my mum watches, because HERMIA was BETROTHED to DEMETRIUS (which meant her dad had

promised his dad that she would marry him) and it was actually AGAINST THE LAW to disagree with your dad in Ancient Athens.

But Hermia HATED Demetrius because he used to pull her hair loads when they were at primary school and he even broke her favourite pen that her gran got her from Turkey. And Hermia loved someone else called LYSANDER and he loved her back and so that was another reason she didn't want to marry Demetrius.

And to make it even WORSE, Hermia's best friend, HELENA, loved DEMETRIUS. But no one loved Helena, except for her

mum, so it was all a bit of a mess.

So Lysander and Hermia decided to run away and live in the woods across the road because they didn't know about the FAIRY WORLD that was in the woods and also because Lysander loved trees and was pretty sure he could make a tree-house using just his bare hands.

But Helena overheard them planning to run away together and decided to tell Demetrius because she thought that might make him like her. But it didn't.

Demetrius was FURIOUS when he found out.

And he said, "I don't even LOVE Hermia but I'm not going to let her dump ME! I'm the

Then Demetrius grabbed his axe and said, "WELL! They won't be able to live in a tree-house if I chop down all the trees, will they? I bet they didn't think of THAT!"

And then he laughed out loud for ages and ran into the woods with the axe.

And even though Demetrius was a bit in

love with himself and had a horrible, scary laugh, Helena ran after him because she liked people like that.

But what Demetrius and the rest of them didn't know was that there was a bit of a drama going on in Fairy World too. So they probably should have stayed FAR AWAY from the woods that day.

Oberon and Titania (the fairy king and queen) had fallen out BIG TIME because Titania used to spend ALL her time with Oberon and cuddle him and make him cheese and crackers and laugh at all his jokes. But then she found a stray cat in the woods one day and she couldn't spend as much time with Oberon any more because she had to make sure the cat was fed and had fresh water and give it lots of attention so it knew it wasn't a stray any more.

Oberon used to watch Titania with the cat and every time she gave it a cuddle he felt JEALOUS because HE wanted the cuddle, and so he said, "I think you love that cat more than you love ME!"

And Titania burst out laughing and said, "Oh, calm down, you big baby. Of course I don't."

So Oberon said, "Fine. Prove it. Give the cat to me and I'll take it to the cat shelter and then it can go back to being just you and me."

But Titania said,

"NEVER!!"

So Oberon stormed out and went and got his most sneaky elf, Puck, to help him play a trick on Titania because he WAS a big baby who was annoyed at his wife for loving a stray cat.

"Go to the shops and get me a flower called

Love-in-idleness," said Oberon. "I've heard that if you squeeze the flower juice into someone's eyes they fall madly in love with the FIRST THING THEY SEE. I'm going to make Titania fall in love with something RIDICULOUS and she will look like a FOOL and THAT will teach her not to ignore ME!"

So Oberon sent Puck to get the flower and he made sure he gave him the exact money because he knew that if he didn't he wouldn't get any change because Puck was sneaky like that.

Oberon made a list of all the things he hoped Titania would see first and fall

DEEPLY in love with. And he REALLY hoped it would be one of his Top Three because they were:

But then Oberon heard a human voice, so

he hid in a bush and made his fairy wings invisible and watched as Demetrius and Helena came running into the woods.

Helena was shouting, "Wait for me! I love you!" And Demetrius was shouting back, "I don't even CARE! I just want to find Hermia. Stop following me!"

Oberon felt sorry for poor Helena because he knew EXACTLY what she felt like and he thought that this "Hermia" was probably another stray cat causing problems and that annoyed him (instead of a human woman who had been told she had to marry a man she didn't like by her dad).

As soon as Puck got back, Oberon asked to see the flower receipt because Puck was eating an ice lolly. But Puck said that he'd lost the receipt because of a lion and Oberon just rolled his eyes and took the flower because Puck was a

NIGHTMARE

sometimes.

"Go and find the young man with long dark hair who just ran past and squeeze the flower juice in his eyes when he's sleeping. I want him to love that poor woman back,"

said Oberon.

But Puck wasn't really paying attention to what Oberon was saying about what the man looked like because he was eating a MINT FEAST and he'd just got to the chocolate bit in the middle, so he ended up going after Lysander (instead of Demetrius) by mistake and putting flower juice in HIS eyes while he slept under a tree with Hermia.

And that's when Helena ran past and she tripped over Lysander's legs and woke him up so she was the first thing he saw.

"KISS ME!" he cried to her. "I love you more than I love water and food and

BREATHING!"

Helena thought Lysander was JOKING, because he was really in love with HERMIA, and he was just making fun of her because nobody ever seemed to like her, so she just called him MEAN and then ran off to find Demetrius.

But Lysander WASN'T joking. So he ran after Helena, and then Hermia woke up and she ran after them both, even though she had NO IDEA what was going on.

(I looked at Zach and he looked like he had NO IDEA what was going on either. So Maisie drew him a diagram while I got on with the story.)

On his way back to Oberon, Puck saw a group of actors from Athens using the woods to rehearse for a play they were doing. One of the actors was called NICK BOTTOM and Puck thought that was funny so he sat and watched for a bit because he still had three Mars bars and a Bounty left in his pocket from the shops because the flower had been in a half-price sale.

Bottom was

TERRIBLE

at acting and he kept forgetting his lines and spitting ALL OVER people when he spoke. And THAT'S when Puck had an idea. He knew that Oberon wanted the queen to fall in love with something **EMBARRASSING** so he decided to use his elf-y magic to give Bottom a **DONKEY'S HEAD** while no one was looking and then make sure he was the first thing Titania saw!

All of the other actors ran away screaming when they saw Bottom's new donkey head on his human body, but Bottom was very confused because there weren't any mirrors in the woods.

That night, Oberon waited until Titania fell asleep and then he put

LOADS

of litter and some worms next to her face.

"She'll be BEGGING ME to break the love spell when she wakes up and falls in love with a WORM or an empty bag of QUAVERS! Ha ha ha ha ha!"

But then Puck explained about the DONKEY-HEADED MAN called BOTTOM and all the SPITTING and Oberon GASPED and said, "Let's DO IT!"

So Puck made himself glow like a firefly and led Bottom to Titania.

Then Oberon threw a stone at Titania to wake her up and ducked behind a bush and covered his mouth to stop himself giggling.

"OUCH!" cried Titania. And then she rubbed her leg for ages.

Oberon got a bit worried that she'd maybe fallen in love with her own LEG but then Bottom said, "HEE-HAW!" and Titania looked up at him and fell

But it turns out it wasn't as funny as Oberon thought it would be, because the fairy queen wasn't embarrassed at ALL. She was in complete

DONKEY-LOVE

with Bottom and she kept stroking his long nose and tickling him under his arms.

Later that night, Oberon heard Helena crying because Demetrius still didn't love her and went to find out what was going on. And that's when Oberon realised that Puck had got it WRONG so he made Puck squeeze

some of the flower juice in Demetrius's eyes while he slept.

But then Lysander turned up, still thinking he was in love with Helena and not Hermia, and cried, "HELENA. You beautiful PEACH!" and Hermia started SCREAMING at Helena because Lysander usually called HER a beautiful peach.

Helena screamed back at Hermia that she HADN'T stolen her boyfriend and that she had NO IDEA what was wrong with Lysander and that she still loved Demetrius.

But Lysander wouldn't stop saying the peach thing and stroking Helena's shoes so

Hermia started picking up mud and throwing it at everyone because she was very confused about what was happening.

And then Demetrius woke up because of all the shouting and saw Helena, and said, "Helena! My LOVE! Let me paint your toenails!" and that made Lysander FURIOUS and he said, "Don't touch her toes! I'LL FIGHT YOU for what you just said to MY Helena!"

And Demetrius grabbed his AXE and said, "LET'S GO THEN!"

So that's when Oberon stepped in and used his fairy-king magic to cover them all in

a thick SLEEPING FOG because he knew that he probably shouldn't have got involved and he didn't want them all to murder each other and

That's when Oberon realised that nothing was really turning out the way he'd expected it to and that the plant Puck had brought back was probably out of date or something.

So Oberon ran back to Titania and gave

her an **EYE BATH** and she stopped loving Bottom and looked up at Oberon and said, "What happened? I had the strangest dream."

And Oberon said that he loved her and that he was sorry about being jealous of the cat. And Titania said that it was OK and that she still wasn't getting rid of the cat but that she would start making him cheese and crackers again like she used to.

So Oberon told Puck to give all the humans eye baths and turn Bottom back into a man. And to check on the cat later because he and Titania were flying out for a meal to celebrate that they were speaking again.

When Lysander woke up he was back in love with Hermia, and Hermia didn't want to throw mud any more.

"I had the weirdest dream," said Lysander, rubbing all the mud off his face.

"Me too!" said Hermia. "I think the woods might be HAUNTED or something! Let's GO!"

But then Demetrius said, "Hermia, you can marry Lysander if you want. In fact, why don't we have a DOUBLE WEDDING!"

And then Demetrius looked at Helena and smiled and Helena gasped with happiness and Puck giggled in the trees because he'd given everyone an eye bath EXCEPT for Demetrius just to see what would happen!

So they all ran back to Athens and had a DOUBLE WEDDING that day.

And they all lived happily ever after until

Demetrius had a shower that night and washed his eyes (but he was already married to Helena by that point so he just went along with it because she wasn't as annoying as he thought she was and she told good jokes).

And that's when Miss Jones spoke into the microphone and said that Gary's mum had donated cakes and juice and that we were to help ourselves.

But when we got to the cake table Maisie screamed, "FAIRY CAKES! The cakes are FAIRY CAKES!"

And that's when we all realised that Gary Petrie had POISONED the fairy cakes with some sort of creepy

LOVE POTION.

So Zach started pouring **LOADS** of cups of poison-diluting juice for Jodi to drink to get rid of the love potion and Maisie started preparing an **EYE BATH**.

But we couldn't get Jodi to come over, even though Maisie was screaming a bit, because Jodi was **OBSESSED WITH DANCING WITH GARY PETRIE** even though they were the only ones still dancing!

And then all of a sudden the lights went

on really bright and the music stopped and Maisie gripped my hand and one of the teachers ran on stage and shouted, "OUR WINNERS!" And everyone started cheering and clapping and someone gave Jodi and Gary a trophy and they both held it for a photo and then Jodi made Gary take his

hand off it and she ran over to us and said, "LOOK! I DID IT! I WON!"

THAT'S when everything made sense and we realised that it had been a DANCE COMPETITION and Jodi had just wanted to WIN because Jodi ALWAYS wants to win and is not really very happy when she doesn't win.

Zach said, "We thought you'd been tricked into eating a fairy cake with a LOVE POTION in it and had fallen in love with Gary Petrie!"

And Jodi looked HORRIFIED and said that she definitely WASN'T in love with Gary

Petrie but that she'd just known that Gary was quite good at dancing and that she had wanted to win the competition. And then we all looked over at Gary Petrie, and his mum and dad were hugging him for winning and he was smiling and picking his nose so Jodi asked to borrow Maisie's antibacterial hand gel.

Then Jodi went over and gave Gary the trophy for a bit because that was the right thing to do and also because Miss Jones gave her a bit of a look. And that's when Gary's mum and dad started hugging Jodi **TOO!**

And Maisie said, "Look at how much Gary's mum and dad like Jodi! Oh NO! Do you think Jodi and Gary are maybe BETROTHED?!"

And we all

ROMEO
and
JULIET

Characters in ROMEO AND JULIET, in order of appearance:

MRS MONTAGUE, Romeo's mum
MRS CAPULET, Juliet's mum
ROMEO MONTAGUE, madly in love with Juliet
ROSALINE, Romeo's crush before Juliet
BENVOLIO, Romeo's friend
PRINCE ESCALUS OF VERONA, ruler of the city
JULIET CAPULET, madly in love with Romeo
TYBALT CAPULET, Juliet's hot-headed cousin
FRIAR LAURENCE, a monk and a friend of Juliet and Romeo
MERCUTIO, Romeo's best friend ever
MR CAPULET, Juliet's dad
PARIS, a foot model

One time my mum and Zach's mum fell out because Zach lives in the flat below us and his mum said that it was TOO LOUD when my mum and dad were having a party.

But my mum said that she WASN'T being too loud at ALL. And also that SHE never complains when Zach's mum has a party.

And that's when our mums fell out

BIG TIME

and it wasn't really because of the noise it was because of the fact that Zach's mum didn't think she'd been invited to the party

(even though she was and I just forgot to give her the invitation like Mum had told me to do).

So the next day I sneaked down to Zach's flat and knocked on the front door and Zach answered and said that he wasn't speaking to me because of his mum not being invited to the party!

So I explained but then Zach's mum appeared and she said that she didn't

BELIEVE ME

and that my mum had probably just sent me

down the stairs to say that.

Then the next day, Zach walked to school **WITHOUT ME** and I had to go in the van with Dad. And at break time Zach wouldn't say

ONE WORD

to me and he kept getting Jodi to pass messages like, "Could you please tell IZZY I am not talking to her," and "Can you please tell IZZY she still has my denim jacket and I need it back by nine o'clock tomorrow," even though we were sitting at the same

table and the denim jacket was from TWO YEARS AGO and wouldn't even FIT him any more.

And that's when I lost my TEMPER and said, "THIS FEUD BETWEEN OUR FAMILIES HAS GONE ON TOO LONG! I don't want to DIE!"

Everyone STARED at me when I said that. And Jodi said, "I don't think you're going to DIE because Zach isn't speaking to you."

And I said, "Really? REALLY?" And I did my WIDE EYES when I said it because I knew that they obviously did not know the story of *Romeo and Juliet*.

So that's when I explained that *Romeo and Juliet* is about a FEUD between two families that ends in

because feuds are dangerous and never really end well.

I told everyone that Mrs Montague used to live in the same street as Mrs Capulet, and that they used to be BEST FRIENDS with each other and say stuff like, "I want my baby to marry your baby when they're all grown up."

But then one day Mrs Montague borrowed Mrs Capulet's hoover, and when she gave it back it was BROKEN and Mrs Montague said it was like that when she got it. But Mrs Capulet said that it DEFINITELY WASN'T and that it was practically BRAND NEW.

After that Mrs Montague and Mrs Capulet fought about EVERYTHING and they

wouldn't let their husbands **OR** their kids speak to each other any more because they had decided they were having a **FULL-ON FEUD**.

But years later, some of the younger generation weren't that bothered about the feud because it had all started years ago when they were babies and they were a bit embarrassed about it actually because of all the arguments and sword fights that would break out everywhere, especially at Parents' Evening if a kid from one family got a better report than a kid from the other.

That's when I told everyone about Romeo

and how he was Mrs Montague's son and that he was OBSESSED with soppiness and being in love and probably roses.

Romeo used to fall in love at least once a week and every time he did he would say stuff like, "I can see stars in her eyes!" and "Oh, my heart feels funny!" and "We should get matching necklaces!"

And one day he fell in love with a girl called Rosaline

even though he had only spoken to her once to ask her to help him tie his shoelaces.

But Rosaline didn't like him back and that was probably because Romeo used to send her about fifty love letters a day and he'd even hand-deliver them to her house and shout "Hi Rosaline!" through her letterbox.

Romeo was

that Rosaline didn't like him back and that he couldn't do all the love letters any more. He wandered around Verona crying and

moaning about his POOR HEART until his friend Benvolio said that he was going to take Romeo to a party to cheer him up.

But the bus had to stop on the way to the party because a HUGE FIGHT broke out on the street between some Capulets and Montagues.

Everyone on the bus tutted and shook their heads at Romeo because they knew he was a MONTAGUE and everyone in Verona was fed up of the feud, especially when it stopped the buses.

And Prince Escalus of Verona was REALLY ANNOYED because it was the third time

that week he'd had to leave his tea and get a taxi down to the city centre to break up one of their fights. So that's when the prince said that if there was

ONE MORE FIGHT

between the two families, then the fighters would be KILLED or maybe just BANISHED from the city FOR LIFE, which means they'd have to go and live in another city like Rome or Manchester.

Once they got to the party Romeo found out that it was a MASKED BALL at MRS CAPULET'S house and that Benvolio had thought it would be funny to sneak in as no one would recognise them because they'd have masks on. And also because he knew that the Capulets ALWAYS served those little prawns with chilli sauce and he wanted some.

And that's when Romeo saw Juliet Capulet. And even though he couldn't see her face because she was wearing a dinosaur mask, Romeo KNEW that he was in LOVE (even though he had been in love with Rosaline

just a minute ago, but that was just the way Romeo was).

Juliet noticed Romeo right away too because he was making heart shapes at her with his hands.

Juliet wasn't completely sure about Romeo to begin with and it was probably because he started crying with happiness the second she asked him to dance with her.

But Juliet danced with him anyway, even though he cried the whole time, because her dad kept trying to get her to dance with someone called Paris and she didn't want to dance with him. And it wasn't just because he was called Paris, it was mostly because her dad was ALWAYS telling her what to do and it was getting on her nerves because she was a teenager.

So anyway, Romeo and Juliet danced all

night and they even made up some dance routines and everyone copied them because they were quite good actually.

By the end of the night Juliet decided that she liked Romeo back because he seemed funny and also because he was wearing a cat mask and she liked cats.

And that's when Romeo realised that he was PROPERLY in love for the first time and that he CARED about Juliet and it was probably because he had had an ACTUAL CONVERSATION with her and that she liked him back (which hadn't really happened to him before).

But just when Romeo was about to go down on one knee and ask Juliet to marry him his cat mask fell off and someone GASPED and it was Juliet's cousin, Tybalt Capulet, and he was

because he recognised Romeo and he shouted at Juliet, "Get away from him! He's a MONTAGUE!"

So Romeo RAN out as fast as he could because he didn't want to get in a fight and end up KILLED or BANISHED because then he'd never see his Baby Cakes again (which is what he called Juliet now).

But instead of just going home, Romeo hid in Juliet's back garden because he loved her SO MUCH that he couldn't bear to be far away from her.

After about an hour Juliet opened her bedroom window to get some air because she had a sore tummy from all the chilli prawns she'd had and that's when Romeo heard her speaking to herself (which some people might find weird but Romeo thought it was cute).

"Romeo, Romeo! Why does he have to

be called Romeo MONTAGUE?" said Juliet. "Why can't he just be called Romeo Thomson or something? Mum and Dad are going to FREAK OUT because I LOVE HIM!"

And that's when Romeo leaped out of the bushes and screamed, "I don't CARE that I'm a Montague and you're a Capulet!

WILL YOU MARRY ME?"

And Juliet said yes, because it turns out she was just as OBSESSED with LOVE as Romeo was and also because Romeo said she could bring all her cats if she liked and that they could be the bridesmaids.

So Romeo threw an engagement ring up to her window that he'd made using **HIS OWN HAIR** when he was hiding in the bushes because he was very arty and a bit weird.

The next day Romeo asked Friar Laurence if he would do the secret wedding because he knew they would have to keep their love a secret because of the **FEUD**.

Friar Laurence said OK but that it had to be **NOW** because the Church Cake Sale was that day. So Romeo **RAN** to get Juliet and Juliet's maid pulled down one of the bedroom curtains and quickly made a

wedding dress from it.

Romeo

COMPLETELY LOST THE PLOT

when he saw Juliet in her wedding dress and he fainted about twenty times before he eventually managed to get down the aisle with the bouquet (he'd always dreamed of doing that and Juliet wasn't really bothered).

Romeo and Juliet kept giving each other little kisses and Friar Laurence eventually had to tell them to stop it and wait for him to say, "You may now kiss the bride" or they wouldn't be properly married.

Romeo gave Juliet ANOTHER horrible hair ring for a wedding ring and then they kissed and did one of their dance routines (even though it was all a bit pointless because there was NO WAY their mums and dads were going to be OK with the marriage because of the feud).

That night Romeo went out for pizza with

his best friend Mercutio because he hadn't had his stag night yet. But then Juliet's cousin TYBALT walked in and ate a WHOLE MARGHERITA PIZZA and STARED at Romeo while he ate it. And EVERYONE knew that meant that he was challenging Romeo to a SWORD FIGHT because Romeo had gatecrashed the Capulet party.

That put Romeo in a bit of an awkward situation since Tybalt was his SECRET COUSIN now because of the secret wedding so he didn't want to fight with his new family, especially on his wedding night.

So Mercutio jumped in to help him out and said, "Fight ME instead!" But Mercutio got distracted during the fighting because Romeo kept asking him if he thought Tenerife was a good place for the honeymoon, and eventually Mercutio got stabbed. And before he died Mercutio screamed, "A plague on both your houses!" because he was really annoyed that he was having to die because

of a stupid feud about a hoover.

Romeo did the BIGGEST GASP anyone has probably ever done when Mercutio got killed and then he screamed for ages because Mercutio was his best friend EVER!

Romeo's mood TOTALLY changed after that. He wanted REVENGE. So he grabbed Mercutio's sword and stabbed Tybalt! And THAT'S when Romeo got his revenge. And ALSO when he realised that he was now DOOMED.

When Friar Laurence saw what Romeo had done he hid him in the church. Romeo was PANICKING because he was about to get

KILLED by the prince or BANISHED FOR LIFE.

But then the friar said to CALM DOWN and he gave Romeo a tent and told him to go and hide in the countryside for a while until everything was sorted out. But Romeo wouldn't go because he said he would miss Juliet too much. So Juliet gave him her cardie and one of her shoes to take with him and he went.

Juliet went home and cried LOADS because she wasn't able to go camping with Romeo. And she got away with all the crying without her mum and dad asking her what was wrong because they thought she was crying because of Tybalt, but she wasn't.

But then Juliet's dad came to see her and said he'd done something to cheer her up and that he'd arranged for her to get MARRIED TO PARIS and that Paris was a foot model and had nice feet and loads of shoes and that the wedding was in two days!

Juliet was STRESSING OUT and she was also FURIOUS because her dad was trying to tell her who to marry and she'd had enough!

So she went to the friar for help. And that's when the friar did something a bit stupid. He gave Juliet a

SLEEPING POTION

that if you took it lasted for two days and made it look like you had DIED when you drank it (even though you were still alive).

Juliet liked the plan because her dad couldn't force her to marry Paris if he thought she was dead. And she knew that when she woke up two days later in her tomb, she could sneak out and get the bus into the countryside and then live happily ever after with Romeo, in the tent.

But the friar said NOT TO TAKE THE POTION UNTIL THE NEXT DAY because he needed to get a message to Romeo first so that he would know Juliet was only PRETEND DEAD and not freak out.

But OBVIOUSLY something went wrong

because

EVERYTHING

goes wrong for Romeo and Juliet because they are DOOMED because of the stupid feud between their families.

When Juliet got home there were loads of cars in the driveway and music playing and then she saw that her dad had brought the red carpet down from the loft and she just KNEW that he was doing the wedding NOW because he was so excited about doing his Father of the Bride speech.

So Juliet took the potion RIGHT AWAY and everyone thought she was dead in the car park because of the Plague.

So the wedding turned into a funeral and the next day it was ALL OVER THE NEWS because Juliet's family were rich and a bit famous.

And even though the friar sent the letter to Romeo by First Class Special Delivery Romeo didn't get it because his tent didn't have a letter box. And when Romeo went to the country shops to buy a magazine because he was bored he saw the picture of JULIET'S FUNERAL ON THE FRONT

PAGE and he screamed,

"NOOOOOOOOOOOOOO!

MY BABY CAKES

IS DEAD!"

and then he ran all the way back to Verona.

Romeo lay next to Juliet in the tomb and cried and cried because he thought she was dead. And then he said that he couldn't BEAR to be without her and that he wanted to stay with her in the tomb FOR EVER so he drank a bottle of poison.

And that is the MOST ANNOYING bit of the story because if Romeo had just CALMED DOWN and stopped CRYING for one minute he would have heard Juliet snoring and seen her drooling a bit and realised that she was actually ALIVE!

As soon as Romeo drank the poison Juliet woke up and gave him a big hug. But then Romeo died. And Juliet screamed,

"NOOOOOOOOOOOOO!"

and tried to drink the poison too but there

wasn't any left so she stabbed herself with Romeo's dagger and died because she had become just as dramatic as Romeo since she got married to him.

Friar Laurence went and got all the Capulets and the Montagues and said, "LOOK at what your stupid feud has done. NOBODY should have to die because of a hoover!"

And then he made them all say sorry and shake hands. And every single Montague and Capulet cried because this was a TRAGEDY and they all promised never EVER to fight again and to be best friends for life. And they should have just done that ages ago

because the whole feud had been pointless. And it just shows that grown-ups can be really stupid and ruin everything sometimes.

And that was the end of the story. Then Jodi grabbed my hand and squashed it into Zach's hand and held both of our hands REALLY TIGHT and said, "I'm not going to let EITHER of you die because of this feud!"

And then she told Zach to say to me, "I'm sorry and I will not ever do a feud with your family ever again," and then she told me to say it too, without blinking, so I did.

That night, everyone came to my house

and we forced Zach's mum and my mum to watch us PERFORM the play of *Romeo and Juliet* and they laughed the whole way through it (even though it wasn't supposed to be funny). And then Jodi did the Hand Thing to them at the end and we all cheered and Mum got the biscuits out because the FEUD was officially over.

Acknowledgements

Retelling Shakespeare's greatest hits is definitely the most fun I've EVER had writing! So I'd like to give a great big, huggy THANK YOU to Marie Crook at the BBC for asking me to take part in the BBC School Radio Shakespeare Retold project, and also to Kate and Kirsty for suggesting I do a whole BOOK of Shakespeare retellings!

Thomas, you are an illustration genius. The cover of TO WEE OR NOT TO WEE! is my favourite cover of ALL the covers EVER. Thank you!

And thanks to my husband, Andy, who now does "Romeo Hearts" at me. It's become a "thing".